Big, Bigger, Biggest

by Susan Ring

STECK-VAUGHN

A Harcourt Company

www.steck-vaughn.com

big boat

bigger boat

biggest boat

bigger boat

big hat

bigger hat

biggest hat

bigger hat

big bear

bigger bear

biggest bear

bigger bear

big ears

bigger ears

biggest ears

bigger ears

big drum

bigger drum

biggest drum

bigger drum

big house

bigger house

biggest house

bigger house

big dog

bigger dog

biggest dog

bigger dog

biggest hug!